# Henry Explores
# the Jungle

# Henry Explores the Jungle

## MARK TAYLOR

*Illustrations by*

## GRAHAM BOOTH

*Atheneum    New York*

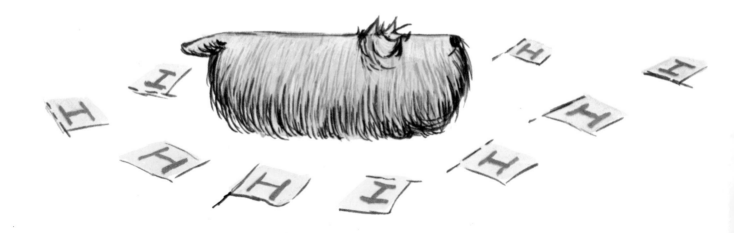

One hot summer morning, Henry and Laird Angus McAngus
read their favorite book about jungles.

"It's time we went exploring in the jungle," said Henry.

Angus wanted to start at once.

"First we have to make preparations," Henry reminded him.

Henry got ready his kit for exploring the jungle.

"This gun is for shooting and catching big game,"
Henry explained to Angus.

Angus wagged his tail happily.

Henry's mother made a lunch for them to take along. "What are you going to explore?" she asked.

"The impenetrable jungle," said Henry. Impenetrable was Henry's favorite new word.

"Is it far from here?" asked his mother.

"It's about half-way around the world," said Henry. "So we have to leave right away."

"Well, don't get eaten by a tiger," she warned.

"We won't," said Henry. "But I expect we'll catch one."

Henry and Angus started out with high hopes.

"This will be a long safari," Henry told Angus.

The grass was taller than Henry and Angus.
But Henry marked their trail with flags.

"We must watch for wild animals and be careful not to
waste food and water," said Henry.

Along the way Henry and Angus discovered
some big game. It was very dangerous. Angus
barked. The cows were terrified. They
ran away while Henry aimed his gun at them.

At the very edge of the jungle, Henry and Angus had an exciting chase.

But when the ram began to chase them, they ran into the jungle and were safe.

It was dark and mysterious in the jungle. Strange rustlings could be heard everywhere.

Henry told Angus not to bark. "If there are tigers here," he said, "we must surprise them."

Henry and Angus came to a pond.
"Every jungle has a swamp," said Henry. "And the
swamps have alligators and snakes in them."

They walked along the swamp and came to a trail. On the trail was a truck that looked like a cage.

"Big game hunters must be here," said Henry.

"What's that?" cried Henry. *"A tiger!"*

Angus began to bark wildly.

Henry ran. Angus ran with him.
They ran right into the cage.

The tiger kept coming after them. Angus
barked fiercely, but the tiger wasn't afraid.

Henry and Angus thought fast.

Quickly they squeezed out between the bars.

Henry ran as fast as he could. Angus removed the pole.
Down slammed the door! The tiger was caught.

Two men came running down the road.
They were very excited.
"Did you see a tiger?" they shouted.

"I caught a tiger," said Henry.
"He's inside this cage."

The men were amazed.
"How did you do it?" they asked Henry.

"It was easy," said Henry. "Angus helped me."

The men explained about the tiger. "He belongs
in the circus," they said. "He was sick and
we took him to the animal hospital. Now we
are taking him back to the circus. But the
door to his cage came loose, and he escaped."

The men gave Henry and Angus a ride home. Henry told them all about exploring. They were very interested.

"We have a lot to learn," they said.

"Well, you must always take flags with you," said Henry, "to make claims and to mark your trail."

When Henry's mother saw them drive up with a real
tiger in the circus truck, she was dumbfounded.

"This is the tiger that Henry caught,"
the men told her.

Everybody had some cake to celebrate
catching the tiger.
Angus had a bone.

"Weren't you afraid?" Henry's mother asked him.

"A little bit," said Henry.
"Sometimes explorers do get frightened,
but that's part of being an explorer."

The men had a reward for Henry and Angus.
It was a ticket to the circus!

"You see," Henry told Angus,
"an explorer's life is a wonderful life."

Angus thumped his tail in agreement.

"Tomorrow, when we go back home," said Henry, "we will have
to go back to the jungle and pick up our flags, in order to…"

"…go exploring again."